The Bear Next Door

Reverie

PUBLISHING COMPANY

The Bear Next Door

Story and pictures by Ginnie Hofmann

This book was originally published by Random House Inc. in 1994.
For additional copies of this book, please contact: Reverie Publishing,
130 Wineow Street, Cumberland, MD 21502; 888-721-4999.
Printed and bound in Korea.

Library of Congress Control Number 2003093610
ISBN 1-932485-03-1

One day, when Andy and his teddy bear, Arthur, came in for dinner, Mother had a big surprise.

"Andy! Daddy has a wonderful new job, and we're going to move!"

"Our new house has a nice yard with a great big apple tree," said Daddy.

"And there's a kid next door named Sam," Mother added.

"That sounds neat," said Andy.

Andy told his best friend, Tom, that he was going to move.

"Mom said there's a boy next door. I sure hope he's fun to play with."

"If you don't like it there," said Tom, "you can come back and live here in our tree house."

When moving day came, Andy and Tom watched the movers fill up the van.

Finally it was time to leave.
"Bye, Tom!" Andy shouted.
"Bye, Andy!"

Daddy followed the big moving van all day long.

At last they reached the new house.

Andy went inside.

"Let's find our new room, Arthur," he said, running up the stairs.

Andy found his room. But when he looked in the closet, he saw an old doll on the floor.

"Ugh!" he cried. "This was a girl's room!"

Andy heard someone calling. When he and Arthur looked out the window, they saw a girl waving to them from the house next door.

"Hi!" she said. "I'm Samantha—you can call me Sam—and this is Emmy, my bear. We can send messages in this basket the way Maryanne and I did."

"No!" Andy shouted. "I don't want any messages from a *girl!*"
"I'm sorry you moved here," Sam answered. "Maryanne and I always sent messages. That is her room, not yours!"

"It is so mine!" cried Andy, and he threw the old doll out
the window!

Sam ran downstairs and picked it up.

"This is Maryanne's doll!" she cried. "You are mean! I sure
don't want *you* for a friend!"

Andy didn't feel like eating supper that night.
"Did you meet Sam?" asked Mother.
"Sam's a girl," said Andy. "Who wants a girl for a friend?"

After supper Andy packed his suitcase.

"Tomorrow we'll go back home, Arthur," said Andy.
"You and I can live in the tree house and play with Tom."
Arthur wasn't sure he wanted to go back.

In the middle of the night, Arthur heard a little voice
calling outside the window. It was Emmy, the bear next door.
"Hi!" she said. "Come on over!"

Arthur put on his red jacket, climbed into the basket,
and pulled the cord.

"Wheee—this is fun!" cried Arthur
as he sailed through the air.

"Shh!" whispered Emmy. "You'll wake Sam."

"Hi. I'm Emmy," said Emmy.

"Hi, Emmy. I'm Arthur," said Arthur.

"I'm glad you moved next door, Arthur," said Emmy.

"Me too!" he said. "But Andy wants to go back home tomorrow and live in his tree house."

"Why can't he build a tree house right in the apple tree?"
Emmy asked. "Then you won't have to leave."

"That's a great idea, Emmy!" whispered Arthur. "Come on,
let's go out and play in the tree."

"We can be a king and queen and live in our castle!"
cried Arthur.

"We'll be pirates and dig for buried treasure!" cried Emmy.

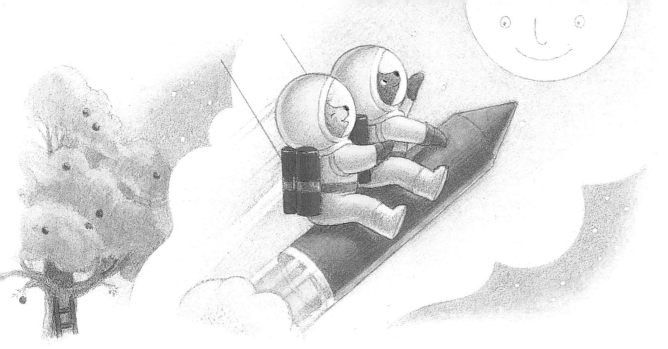

"Let's play astronauts and fly to the moon!" said Arthur.

Arthur and Emmy were getting tired. They found a cozy
place to sleep in the big apple tree.

The next morning Andy
couldn't find Arthur.

He wasn't under the bed. . .

Or in the closet. . .

"Maybe I left him in
the yard," thought Andy.

That morning Sam couldn't find Emmy.

She wasn't behind the fishbowl. . .

Or under the dresser. . .

"Maybe I left her in the yard," thought Sam.

Andy ran outside. Sam was there too.

"I can't find Emmy anywhere," she cried.

"I can't find Arthur, either," said Andy. "Come on, Sam. Let's go look for our bears!"

And off they went!

Sam looked in the flower bed, but the bears weren't there.

Andy looked in Spot's house, but the bears weren't there.

"I'm afraid we've lost them," he said sadly.

Suddenly Spot began to bark.

"There they are!" Sam shouted. "Up in the apple tree!"

Andy brought the bears down. "I wonder what they were
doing in the tree," he said.

Sam laughed. "Maybe they wanted to build a tree house!"

"Sam!" cried Andy. "That's a great idea. Let's build one!"
"Super!" said Sam. "I'll get my tools."

And so Andy and Sam built a wonderful tree house in the big apple tree.

Sam said, "I'm glad you moved next door, Andy."

"Me too," said Andy.

Who's happy to have a new friend now?
Andy is!